# Oh My Goddess!

あああっ女神さまっ **28**

### STORY AND ART BY
## Kosuke Fujishima

#### TRANSLATION BY
### Dana Lewis AND Christopher Lewis

#### LETTERING AND TOUCH-UP BY
### Susie Lee AND Betty Dong WITH Tom2K

**DARK HORSE MANGA™**

# CHAPTER 177
# Little Voice, Great Sorrow

HMPH...
I *KNEW*
IT WAS
AN
"AHEM
BUG."

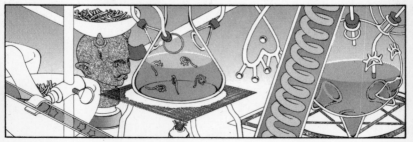

SQUIISH

GLOOP

plop

...SO MAKE SURE YOU DRINK THIS.

I'VE REMOVED IT, BUT THE SYMPTOMS WILL LINGER...

YOUR PRESCRIP-TION!

RIGHT.

FOR INTERNAL GODDESS USE ONLY

KLUNK

TAKE CARE, NOW!

BOMF

OKAY

...SO YOU WON'T GET YOUR VOICE BACK 'TILL THREE.

IT'LL TAKE ABOUT SIX HOURS TO WORK...

OH...

AH...

...

...I'LL GO TAKE MY MEDI-CINE.

10

BIG SISTER, I DON'T WANT YOU TO DRINK *THIS!*

THEY'LL CALL OUT THE ARMY TO STOP YOU!!

WHAT IF IT TURNS YOU INTO A *TOAD?* OR A *GIANT TOAD?!*

I MEAN, *C'MON...* MEDICINE FROM *URD?!*

...real-ly?

AH...

IT'S OKAY.

OUR BIG SISTER'S MEDICINE WORKS WHEN IT WORKS, DOESN'T IT?

...HOLD ON A MINUTE.

...YESSSS...

WHY...

AH, THAT'S NO GOOD...

NOT LISTENING ↓

...

I'M OKAY...

YOUR VOICE?

...WHAT?

NOW, OPEN WIDE...

I SHALL GIVE YOU MY ESSENCE DE ROSE!

NISHIMORI WEST MIDDLE SCHOOL INTERSECTION

YES, THAT'S RIGHT...

sp-ishh

sp-ishh

AH...

BRMB
BRMB
BRMB
BRMB
BRMB
BRMB
BRMB
BRMB
BRMB
BRMB

HUH?

WHAT?

I'VE JUST LOST MY VOICE.

...

ARE YOU OKAY? SHOULDN'T YOU TAKE THE DAY OFF?

?

I'M OKAY.

...LOOK AT *THIS!!*

OH...

UHM...

EH...

ISN'T IT *CUTE?!*

IT'S A *CAM\**, YOU SEE?

CHECK OUT THE "O" IN "WEL-COME" ...?

*Not "cam" as in "camera," but "cam" as in "rotating wheel or shaft that strikes a lever at one or more points along a circular path."

...HOW 'BOUT *YOU*, BELL?

WHAT SORT OF RESPONSE IS *THAT?*

...IT'S *NICE.*

WELL, I MEAN, YEAH...

I THINK IT'S CUTE.

...

WAHHH! I KNEW IT WASN'T CUTE!!!

NO, NO, NO! SHE'S JUST LOST HER VOICE! IT'S *ALSO* TRUE THAT IT'S NOT CUTE, BUT...

...IT WASN'T GETTING A GOOD RESPONSE ANYWAY.

...IT'S ALL RIGHT...

...I'M SORRY.

AH... AHH..

AH...

--WHAT DID YOU WANT TO TELL US...?

...THE RUSH SEASON, RIGHT?

IT'S...

TEN ?! !!

...

SO HOW MANY'D YOU GET THIS YEAR?

OH, YEAH! I GUESS IT *IS* THAT TIME.

I MEANT *ZERO!!* *NOBODY* WANTS TO JOIN THE MOTOR CLUB!!

THAT'S *AMAZING*, HASEGAWA!! IT'S A NEW *RECORD!!*

THAT'S WHY I *CAME* TO CONSULT YOU!!.

SHAKKA SHAKKA SHAKKA SHAKKA

WHAT ARE YOU GONNA *DO*, HASEGAWA?! YOU'RE IN *TROUBLE!!*

23

GO GIVE THEM A HAND.

MORI-SATO...

THE MOTOR CLUB'S IN *CRISIS!!*

IS IT REALLY OKAY ...?

TH...

...THANK YOU *SO MUCH* !!

BELLDANDY, WILL YOU HELP US, TOO?

BUT WHAT HURTS *MOST*...

...JUST NOW, I WASN'T ABLE TO USE MY SPELLS--

...SHOULD IT WORRY ME SO MUCH?

JUST LOSING MY VOICE...

I'M WORRIED...

...FOR NOT BEING ABLE TO SING.

...IS GRIEVING...

...THAN FOR FAILING HASEGAWA.

...I FEEL WORSE ABOUT *THAT*...

# OH MY GODDESS!
## B E L L D A N D Y

GO GIVE THEM A HAND.

THE MOTOR CLUB'S IN CRISIS!!

THAT'S WHAT SHE SAID, BUT...

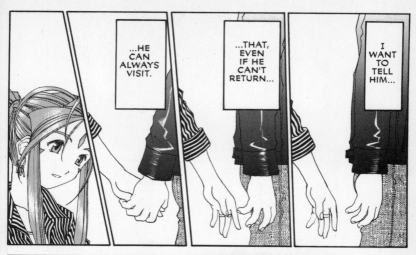

34

...MY FEELINGS *STILL* REACH HIM.

...um...SO WHAT HAVE YOU BEEN TRYING SO FAR...?

AH, SORRY, SORRY...

...BUT WHAT ABOUT THE NEW MEMBER CAMPAIGN ...?

SORRY TO INTERRUPT YOUR *LOVE SCENE*...

...THE UPPER-CLASSMEN MADE THEM...

UM... Y'KNOW... POSTERS... FLIERS...

EXAMPLES

NO. I'D DIE FIRST.

WOULD THIS MAKE YOU WANT TO JOIN?

YES?

HASE-GAWA.

HOW CAN WE GATHER A BUNCH OF PEOPLE...

BECAUSE I'D PROBABLY *ALSO* DIE IF I TOOK IT *DOWN!!*

*THEN WHY'D YOU LEAVE IT UP?*

YEAH. *LET'S.*

...LET'S THINK OF SOME-THING ELSE...

HOW? *HOW?* STILL DA VOICE OF *UNCERTAINTY,* MORISATO!

...THE SHADOW OF DOOM.

OH...

--WHAT, ON ANOTHER BRILLIANT FLYER ...?

WE'VE BEEN HARD AT WOIK!!

uh-huh.

FU... AL
TIMES! PRIZES!

CONTEST

R.I.P.

Heavenly voices
beckon you at our
...e tent!!!

...PEOPLE WILL GATHER FOR *THAT?*

*SEMPAI...* DO YOU REALLY THINK...

B-B-BURIAL CUSTOMS FROM AROUND THE WORLD?

WHAT? SH-SH-SHOW AND TELL?

D-D-DID THAT FLYER SAY *FUNERAL* CONTEST ?!?

YEAH! JUST LEAVE IT TO *US!*

HUH? WHY *WOULDN'T* DEY?

...I'D PREFER *NOT* TO DO...

THAT'S SOME-THING...

WHO'S FIRST ...?!

...LET'S OPEN WITH SOME MUSIC!

WE'LL GET INTO OUR CLUB LATER, BUT FOR NOW...

KARAOKE CONTEST

HELLO, EVERYONE! WELCOME TO THE N.I.T.M.C. KARAOKE CONTEST!!

THIS WHOLE THING-- THEY JUST WANTED TO SING--!

DO YA HAVE TA ASK? IT'S THE CHARMIN' COMBO OF MIYA AND TAKKI ...!!!

..."THE MEASURE OF A MAN"!

CHUKKA CHUKKA CHUKKA

CHUKKA

AND WE'S GONNA DO A LITTLE NUMBER FOR YA CALLED...

41

...huh?

...THEY'RE *STAYING* !!

WAIT... THEY'RE IN *PAIN*, BUT...

WHAT?! DIS THING'S *BUSTED*!

IT MUST BE. IT WASN'T ZERO.

TWELVE POINTS!! CONGRAT-ULATIONS !!

CHAKKA CHAKKA

LET'S SEE HOW THEY *DID!*

THANK YOU VERY MUCH!

EVEN WHEN YOU'VE LOST SIGHT OF TOMORROW--

RACKE

NUMBER 2 ON THE MIC-- HANJI ANNAKA!

WORD TO THE MOTHER!

NUMBER 3'S GOING TO SING "SAKURA WATER-WORKS"!

WHY ARE THEY *TRYING* SO HARD ...?

...I COULD SING LIKE THEM.

AHH, I WISH...

AND *I'M* SINGING ♪ "LOVE SOLUTION." ♪♪

I'M NUMBER 5!!

SORA... I'LL BE THE ONE TO PROTECT YOUR LIPS.

crackle

fuuuume

FROM *WHAT?*

PROTECT HER *LIPS?*

45

(SOME ON HASE-GAWA)

ALL THEIR EYES ARE *FIXED*...

...ON *BELL-DANDY!!*

...WHAT DID YOU MEAN BY *LIPS?*

WAIT A SEC...

THANK YOU VERY MUCH--

heavenly voice
ckon you at o
karaoke tent!!

y female club
mber's kiss ❤
**OR**
Scooter
year's worth!)

le club
kiss ❤
?
er
worth!)

...THE
FLYER
?!

DIDN'T
YOU
READ...

**FUN** TIMES! **REAL** PRIZES!

**CONTEST**

RIP
INTO
YOUR
FAVE
SONG

Heavenly voices
beckon you at our
karaoke tent!!!

Any female club
member's kiss ×
**OR**
Scooter
(One year's worth!)

YOU
DIDN'T
KNOW
...?

WHAT
THE
HECK IS
*THIS*--!!

...I
THOUGHT
EVERYONE
WOULD GO FOR
*BELLDANDY.*

HUH?

*HASEGAWA!*
HOW
COULD
YOU
*GO FOR
THIS?!*

47

48

...OR DO YOU WANT THE ONE YEAR'S WORTH OF SCOOTER?

OH... N-NO... N-NOT FOR THE PRIZE...

WHAT?

WHAT DOES *THAT* MEAN?

ONE FOR EACH DAY OF THE YEAR, OR SOMETHING?

RIP INTO YOUR FAVE SONG

Hea... beckon... karaoke te...

Any female club member's kiss ×
**OR**
Scooter
(One year's worth!)

ONE YEAR'S *WORTH* OF SCOOTER?

ONE YEAR'S WORTH SCOOTER!

IT'S OVER *THERE.*

ONE YEAR'S WORTH SCOOTER

...DEAD.

SO, NO MATTER WHO WINS, WE'RE...

I'M GONNA GET ME ONE YEAR'S WORTH OF SCOOTER! WHATEVER *THAT* MEANS!

NO WONDER THERE'S GIRLS OUT THERE...

FWAP

BUT I'VE GOTTA WIN... EVEN IF IT KILLS ME!!

YOU GOTTA WIN...EVEN IF IT KILLS YOU!!

# CHAPTER 179

# What Can I Do For You

54

WOW! THE BEST SO FAR!!

BOOOO!

heh heh heh

I WANT TO SING...

NOW, COMING UP NEXT IS...

I WANT TO SING, TOO...

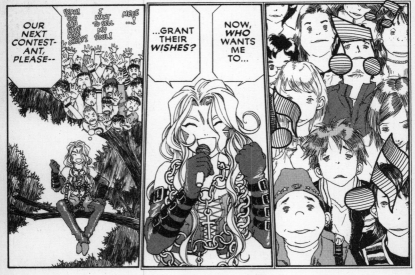

58

BELLDANDY'S LIPS SHALL BE *MINE!*

...OH YEAH, RIGHT... OF COURSE...

NOBODY MADE A *REQUEST,* BUDDY.

SING IT AND GET OUT OF HERE.

...I'LL SING "TYPHOON EYES."

YOU STILL ALIVE, AOSHIMA...?

...SHE SEEMS TO HAVE NOTICED HOW *ATTRACTIVE* I AM!

HMM ...!

*I want to sing...*

*I want to sing...*

*I want to sing...*

*I want to sing...*

...RIGHT!

...

OH...

MISS BELLDANDY! CAN YOU *SING* FOR US?

...YOU WON'T GET YOUR VOICE BACK 'TILL THREE.

UHM...

...3:12.

...ORDINARILY, THAT WOULD BE A *BRILLIANT* IDEA, BUT...

WELL, HASE-GAWA...

Which means...

What time is it?

64

...IT FEELS LIKE I HAVEN'T HEARD IT FOR AGES.

BELL-DANDY'S VOICE...

THE *SWITCH*--!

*WAIT!*

--NO!

S-SOMEBODY... HELP...

H-HOW LONG HAS SHE BEEN ON...?

50th SONG

10th SONG

20th SONG

...BUT ...BUT I WANT TO HEAR *MORE*...

*wobble*

STOP...

STOP...

DON'T STOP...

DON'T STOP...

30th SONG

40th SONG

...AND ...NICE WORK, HASE-GAWA.

SLEEP TIGHT, BELL-DANDY.

ZZZZZ

Ping

THE

HUH?

*SIDE* EFFECTS?

EVERYBODY *HYPNOTIZED?*

...AND I HEARD NOTHING.

HMM! WELL, THERE ARE CERTAIN *CONTRA-INDICATIONS*... SUPPOSE SOMEONE MIXED IN SOMETHING ELSE...

WELL, HOW DO YOU EXPLAIN THIS?

*uh-uh!* MY MEDICINE COULDN'T CAUSE THAT.

...OR NEVER SHOWED UP.

...ALMOST EVERYONE WHO SIGNED ON EITHER *CANCELLED*...

WHEN EVERYONE CAME TO THEIR *SENSES*...

CAN'T STOP... THE MUSIC!

...NOT MANY KNEW THERE WAS A *DEMON MEMBER*, TOO.

BUT...

**CHAPTER 180**

# The Polka-Dotted Cat and the Magic Broom

MM?!

HSSS!!

WHSSHTT

...IT'S *YOU*, VELSPER.

OH...

WHAT THE HECK... I MEAN, *HELL?!*

flip flop

OH, MY...

I THOUGHT YOU WERE A CATER-PILLAR, HERE TO EAT MY LOVELY ROSES.

...I'M *SO* SORRY.

BUT SURELY *BELL-DANDY* WILL...

...THEY'RE ALL MAKING *FUN* OF ME...

...MAYBE WE NEED TO PRIME THE PUMP.

CHAK CHAK

I CHANGED THE PACKING, BUT...

PLEASE ALLOW ME...

Thou Spirits of Water Flowing Deep Beneath the Earth...

OH ...!

BRBLBRBL

I'LL GET YOU A *TOWEL!*

--!! I'M SORRY!! I OVER-DID IT!!

SPOOSH

'M OKAY.

THANKS.

...AND IT'S NO SOLUTION.

THAT WILL ONLY PUT YOU OFF BALANCE AGAIN...

NO.

...MAYBE WE OUGHT TO RETURN HER TO ME.

BESIDES, *YOU GAVE THIS FAMILIAR TO ME...*

...SO I CAN *NEVER* GIVE IT BACK.

...OKAY.

NOT FOR *FREE*, THAT'S FOR SURE!!

DO *US* A FAVOR?

...AND IF SHE *WILL* DO IT, EVEN AT A PRICE...

WE WON'T KNOW FOR SURE UNTIL WE ASK...

SO *DON'T*...

WE'LL TAKE CARE OF IT *SOMEHOW*!

...BUT ARE THINGS REALLY GETTING ANY BETTER ...?

...WE DON'T EVEN KNOW WHERE SHE *IS!!*

B-BUT...

BUT YOU'RE JUST GUESS-ING!

...SHE'S NOT SO FAR...

I IMAG-INE...

94

...MAY I ASK YOU A FAVOR?

H-H-H-HOW'D YOU KNOW I WAS *HERE?!*

... ...

I *WON'T.*

CAN YOU CURE--

HE MUST WORK FOR YOU, RIGHT?

WELL, THERE WAS A FLY ON MY WALL.

95

98

snort

*wriggle*
*wriggle*

*twitch*
*twitch*

**HAHA HAHA HAHA!!**

*pound pound*

!!

IT WAS SO FUNNY I DON'T *MIND* HELPING... *BUT...*

*OH,* WHAT A GOOD LAUGH THAT WAS.

...WILL SHE ASK FOR *ME* AGAIN ...?

...*IF* YOU PLAY ME AND WIN.

LET'S SAY I'LL HELP...

102

# CHAPTER 181

# Fastest Broom, Greatest Race!

BUT *WAIT!* THERE'S *MORE!*

THAT'S A *VACUUM CLEANER* !!

YES, BUT NOW HOW MUCH WOULD YOU PAY?

*I* WANT ONE!

WHAT IS THIS? *TV SHOP-PING?!*

NO MESSY BAGS TO EMPTY...

*fwoosh*

...HOW *ABOUT* IT?

AND SO...

...YOU, *TOO* ...?

HOW WONDER-FUL... ♥♥

LET'S RACE.

OKAY.

MY...

...A GOOD ANSWER.

...WHAT'S WRONG?

*shiver shiver*

...Y-YES, MA'AM...

LET'S TRY OUR BEST! ♥

THERE'S *NO* BROOM THAT CAN BEAT IT.

WHAT?

...THE *FASTEST EVER.*

IS...

*GLÜHENDE HERZ...*

...THE *FASTEST* IN *HEAVEN.* ...OR SO HE SAYS.

WELL, STRING-FELLOW HAWKE'S...

ITS SPEED IS *DAZZLING.*

*PERHAPS...* BUT STILL NOT AS FAST AS HERS.

I DO.

YOU TALK AS IF YOU KNOW IT.

IT USED TO BE *MINE*.

...AND SAIL THROUGH IT LIKE A *BLADE*...

I REMEMBER THE TIMES WHEN I WOULD BREAK INTO HEAVEN...

*WHAT ?!*

MY
FASTEST
*PARTNER*--

MA'AM, WE HAVEN'T A CHANCE.

um...

WELL, THEN I GUESS *YOU'RE* OUT OF LUCK, TOO...

THERE'S NOT A *CHANCE* SHE CAN WIN.

NO. *FASTER.*

--IS IT *REALLY* THAT FAST?

hugg ♥

EVEN IN *HEAVEN.*

*WHY NOT? GLÜHENDE HERZ* IS A *LEGEND.*

WHY NOT?

I'LL DO IT!!

N-N-NEVER!

WELL, THEN.

LET'S
GO.

YES,
MA'AM!

SO, LET'S SET THE COURSE.

...THEN *UNDER* THOSE THREE BRIDGES...

THE *TORII* GATE OF THE SHRINE...

THROUGH THAT RED GATE TO THE TOP OF THE HILL.

LEFT AT THE SMOKE-STACK.

...WHAT DO YOU SAY?

WELL...

...AND LASTLY, THE *WINNER* MUST *TOLL THE BELL.*

...THEN A *TELEPHONE POLE SLALOM...*

UNDER-STOOD.

SO, YOUNG KEIICHI. GET US *GOING,* mm?

IF *YOU* LOSE, YOU *ALL* GO BACK TO HEAVEN.

?

AND I NEARLY FORGOT.

WHAT?!!

!!

REALLY, NOW. A BET *IS* A MUTUAL CONTRACT, YES? ♥

WELL?

AND IT'S *YOUR* FAULT IF YOU DON'T ASK ALL THE TERMS.

I HAVE NO REASON TO OBJECT.

THAT'S RIGHT.

....

...

...THERE'S NO WAY THAT I *WILL* LOSE.

BECAUSE...

...WELL, IF BELLDANDY SAYS SO.

HUH?

REALLY?

*huh?*

LEND ME YOUR EAR...

WHAT? WHY?

COME HERE A SECOND.

WAIT! *WAIT!*

THEN, ON YOUR MARK...

HOW'D YA LIKE MY *DEMON KISS?!*

!!

CHING

P·l·p

WHAT-WHAT-WHAAAT?!

QUITE THE GIRL, BELLDANDY.

...I UNDERESTIMATED YOUR CONCENTRATION.

WHOOME

BUT, MY *DEAR*...

WHOOOSH

...YOU HAVEN'T EVEN *SEEN* ITS POWER YET.

# OH MY GODDESS!
## BELLDANDY

# CHAPTER 182
# Courage and Trial

UH? YEAH, SURE...

DON'T BE DUMB. OF *COURSE* SHE'S OKAY.

IS SHE REALLY OKAY ...?

BUT *BELL-DANDY? RACING?*

huh?

...YOU DIDN'T EVEN *KNOW?!*

133

...BELL-DANDY'S WON THE BROOM RACE CHAMPION-SHIP.

UP IN *HEAVEN*...

...BUT IS EVEN *THAT* ENOUGH?

HUH?

*SIX* TIMES.

STOP SAYING THAT.

*HUH* ?!

...THE *EIGHT-TIME* CHAMPION OF THE DEMON WORLD.

*GLÜHENDE HERZ* IS...

135

136

heh-
heh...

...YOU HAVEN'T SEEN *GLÜHENDE HERZ'S* REAL *SPEED.*

THAT WAS IN A *TURN...*

SHE *DID* IT! *THAT'S* MY BIG SISTER!

144

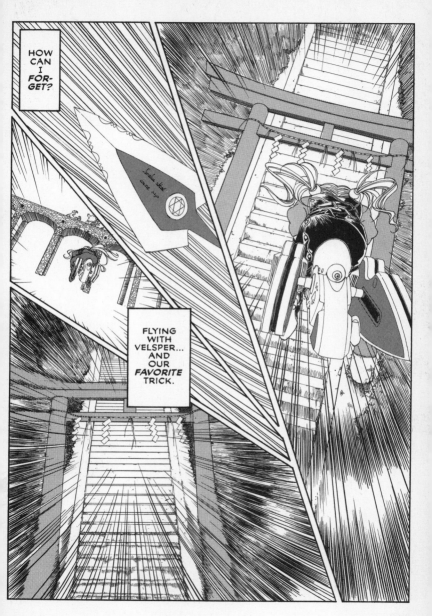

146

I...
I'M
SORRY.

...I D-DIDN'T
THINK
THEY'D
DARE GO
THROUGH
WITHOUT
SLOWING
DOWN...

148

GRpp

!!

BUT HILD'S HEADING DOWN... SHE'S FLYING *NAPE-OF-THE EARTH!*

EH?

WE'LL KEEP CLIMB-ING!

IT'S OKAY! *TRUST* ME!

....AND *ACCELERATE* WHILE WE CAN?

WOULDN'T IT BE BETTER TO USE OUR *POTENTIAL ENERGY...*

THAT'S RIGHT...

...*LADY BELLDANDY* IS FLYING ME...

FORGIVE US FOR BUZZING YOUR SHRINE.

...THERMALS
!!

...YES...THIS
TIME OF
THE YEAR...
ON THIS
MOUNTAIN-
SIDE...
THERE ARE
*ALWAYS*
THERMALS.

...BUT THEY HELP *US* CLIMB.

...AND THEY MAY SLOW *YOU* DOWN...

BUT YOU KNOW WHAT?

WELL, YOU'RE JUST FULL OF SURPRISES.

SHOOMP

!!

154

IT'S BRIDGES ALL THE WAY. CAN YOU KEEP UP...

...WITH NO BRAKES?!

**EDITOR**
Carl Gustav Horn

**DESIGNER**
Scott Cook

**ART DIRECTOR**
Lia Ribacchi

**PUBLISHER**
Mike Richardson

English-language version
produced by Dark Horse Comics

OH MY GODDESS! Vol. 28
©2007 Kosuke Fujishima. All rights reserved. First published
in Japan in 2004 by Kodansha, Ltd., Tokyo. Publication rights for
this English edition arranged through Kodansha Ltd. This English-
language edition ©2007 by Dark Horse Comics, Inc. All other material
©2007 by Dark Horse Comics, Inc. All rights reserved. No portion of this
publication may be reproduced or transmitted, in any form or by any
means, without the express written permission of the copyright holders.
Names, characters, places, and incidents featured in this publication either
are the product of the author's imagination or are used fictitiously. Any
resemblance to actual persons (living or dead), events, institutions, or
locales, without satiric intent, is coincidental. Dark Horse Manga™
is a trademark of Dark Horse Comics, Inc. All rights reserved.

Published by Dark Horse Manga
a division of Dark Horse Comics, Inc.
10956 SE Main Street
Milwaukie, OR 97222
www.darkhorse.com

To find a comics shop in your area,
call the Comic Shop Locator Service
toll-free at 1-888-266-4226

First edition: December 2007
ISBN: 978-1-59307-857-7

1 3 5 7 9 10 8 6 4 2

Printed in Canada

# letters to the
# ENCHANTRESS

10956 SE Main Street, Milwaukie, Oregon 97222
omg@darkhorse.com • www.darkhorse.com

*NOTE: Full addresses and e-mail addresses will not be printed, unless you ask! All fan artwork, letters, and e-mails submitted become the property of Dark Horse Comics.*

We'll start this installment of *Letters to the Enchantress* with something I'm well experienced with—saying sorry. Of course, we didn't run letters and fan art last time because of the sneak preview for Yumi Tohma's *Oh My Goddess!—First End* novel. But recently we found some correspondence from Chris Smigliano and Doris Kwan that was actually sent to us by e-mail way back in *February!* Somehow it got misrouted, and please accept my apologies: we only have room for Chris's letter this time, but Doris's work will be coming up in Vol. 8! As you know, we switch off between old and new volumes . . .

Dear *OMG!* Staff:

Just a quick note to tell you how much I'm enjoying this series. I must admit, however, I'm a recent convert to the church of Belldandy. My local library started to carry manga and graphic novels a couple years ago and I was finally intrigued enough to take a look. I was aware of *OMG!*'s exsistence before, but figured the series might not be to my taste.

Boy, was I wrong!

This series is great loopy fun, all at once funny and dark and heartwarming. And of course I had to glom onto the OVA and TV series (ADV Films—not Media Blasters—will be releasing the second TV season on DVD, BTW). But I'm really hoping sales continue to be good enough that DH releases the whole manga series. It's kind of interesting comparing the translations between the "Flopped" and "Unflopped" Versions.

And of course, Mr. Kosuke's artwork . . . what can you say about anyone that can draw both intricate machinery AND lovely ladies? Of, course, we all have our favorites amongst the *OMG!* cuties . . . I've enclosed a sketch of mine below.

Keep up the good work!

Chris Smigliano
(For Art's Sake: *COMICS BUYERS GUIDE*)

Well, we've been putting out the English version of *Oh My Goddess!* since 1994 (before some of our readers were born!) and we're now up to Vol. 28, so we have no intention of stopping anytime soon—thanks to everyone's longtime support!

I've been a fan of Megumi Morisato since the moment she first showed up at the end of Vol. 1. Maybe it's because my own sister went to the same college I did (although she's three minutes *older*), and is a mechanically savvy motorcyclist. She has kind of an Indiana Jones perspective on life—that you should know how to do everything, because "what if you had to?" So she learned how to ride a motorcycle, drive a car, fly a plane, ride a horse, etc., just in case she has to make a getaway and one of the above is the only method available.

So naturally I loved the crazed techno-contest between Megumi and Skuld in Vol. 6 of *Oh My Goddess!*, and of course I could relate to Keiichi's conflicted nostalgia at the campus festival in this volume—a side effect of switching off between old and new volumes is being able to look at my own college days both in the present and the past. If you like this aspect of the story, you might want to check out sometime another great 1980s comedy set at an engineering school, *Real Genius*. The dorm scenes were shot at my school, Pomona College—even though the campus itself was much closer to Pomona's pal, Harvey Mudd (I know the film was in fact inspired by Harvey Mudd's arch-rival, Cal Tech, but that's a twenty-minute commute). While there are no goddesses in it, the main female character, Jordan, is *sort of* like Skuld's mind under Megumi's haircut. Notice the italics and the underlining.

—CGH

MEGUMI © KOSUKE FUJISHIMA

# Kosuke Fujishima's Oh My Goddess!

Dark Horse is proud to re-present *Oh My Goddess!* in the much-requested, affordable, Japanese-reading, right-to-left format, complete with color sections, informative bonus notes, and your letters!

 $10.95 each!

AVAILABLE AT YOUR LOCAL COMICS SHOP OR BOOKSTORE
*To find a comics shop in your area, call 1-888-266-4226

For more information or to order direct:
•On the web: darkhorse.com
•E-mail: mailorder@darkhorse.com
•Phone: 1-800-862-0052 Mon.–Fri. 9 A.M. to 5 P.M. Pacific Time.

# STOP! This is the back of the book!

This manga collection is translated into English, but arranged in right-to-left reading format to maintain the artwork's visual orientation as originally drawn and published in Japan. If you've never read comics this way before, take a look at the diagram below to give yourself an idea of how to go about it. Basically, you'll be starting in the upper right-hand corner, and will read each word balloon and panel moving right-to-left. It may take a little getting used to, but you should get the hang of it very quickly. Have fun! If this is the millionth manga you've read this way, never mind. ^_^